KU-167-076

THIS BOOK BELONGS TO

. . . .

This edition published by Parragon Books Ltd in 2017

Parragon Books Ltd
Chartist House
15–17 Trim Street
Bath BA1 1HA, UK
www.parragon.com

Copyright © 2017 DC Comics.
JUSTICE LEAGUE and all related characters and elements © & ™ DC Comics.
WB SHIELD: ™ & © Warner Bros. Entertainment Inc. (s17)

All rights reserved. No part of this publication may be reproduced, stored in a retrieval system
or transmitted, in any form or by any means, electronic, mechanical, photocopying, recording
or otherwise, without the prior permission of the copyright holder.

ISBN 978-1-5270-0087-2

Printed in Italy

JUSTICE LEAGUE™

ANNUAL 2018

CONTENTS

08 .... THE JUSTICE LEAGUE
10 .... PROFILE: BATMAN
11 .... KNIGHT WATCH
12 .... SIGN OF THE CRIMES
13 .... MISSING IN ACTION!
14 .... PROFILE: SUPERMAN
15 .... ODD HERO OUT
16 .... SUPERMAN SUDOKU
17 .... MAN OF STEEL WORD SEARCH
18-25 .... STORY: STARRO AND STRIPES FOREVER
26 .... PROFILE: WONDER WOMAN
27 .... WARRIOR PRINCESS
28 .... VISION QUEST
29 .... OUT OF SORTS
30 .... PROFILE: GREEN LANTERN
31 .... MYSTERY MEMO
32 .... POWER PAIRS
33 .... RING ROBBER
34-41 .... STORY: THE RETURN OF STARRO
42 .... PROFILE: THE FLASH
43 .... THE FLASH DASH
44 .... SPOT THE SPEEDSTER
45 .... NEED FOR SPEED
46-47 ... ALIEN INVADERS
48 .... PREPARE FOR BATTLE
49 .... CROSSING THE ENEMY
50-58 ... STORY: DAY OF THE UNDEAD
59 .... FREEZE FRAME!
60-61.... WANTED: GALAXY DEFENDER
62 .... DOUBLE TROUBLE!
63 .... COMIC CREATOR!
64-68 ... POSTERS
69 .... ANSWERS

THE JUSTICE LEAGUE

Say hello to the bad guys' worst enemy... a team made up of the world's most powerful super heroes. Their aim? To be Earth's first line of defence against any threat!

SUPERMAN

Who is he: The strongest, most formidable being in the world.

BATTER UP!

How many of Batman's batarangs can you spot on these two pages?

WONDER WOMAN

Who is she: One of Earth's most powerful defenders of peace, truth and equality.

Answer on page 69

THE FLASH

Who is he: The fastest man alive and a founding member of the league.

GREEN LANTERN

Who is he: A galactic police officer who fights evil with the aid of his Power Ring.

BATMAN

Who is he: A masked hero who operates on the mean streets of Gotham City.

DID YOU KNOW?

There have been lots of different Justice League members over the years, from *Blue Beetle* and *Hawkgirl* to *Cyborg* and *Aquaman*.

CYBORG

AQUAMAN

HAWKGIRL

BLUE BEETLE

9

PROFILE:

BATMAN

Real name: Bruce Wayne

Also known as: The Caped Crusader, The Dark Knight

Place of birth: Gotham City

Occupation: Billionaire, businessman, crime fighter

Strengths: Brilliant detective, supreme athlete and martial artist, hugely wealthy

Weaknesses: Walks the line between light and dark

Enemies: The Joker, Bane, Two-Face, Killer Croc, The Penguin, The Riddler

In his own words: "To the Batmobile!"

BATMAN IN ACTION

Batman has a huge collection of hi-tech weapons and gadgets, which he uses to protect the people of Gotham City – and occasionally, Metropolis.

DID YOU KNOW?

Batman lives in an enormous mansion known as Wayne Manor.

The Batmobile

Night Vision Binoculars

Underwater Breathing Device

Grappling Hook

KNIGHT WATCH

Batman is protecting the night-time Gotham City streets. Can you peer through the gloom and work out which outline belongs to the real Dark Knight?

Answer on page 69

SIGN OF THE CRIMES

Guide Batman through the maze to the Bat-Signal. Your route must go through all six villains without retracing your steps. Strike a big cross on each foe as you pass him!

Answer on page 69

MISSING IN ACTION!

The Batmobile urgently needs some new parts.
Which three jigsaw pieces complete the picture?

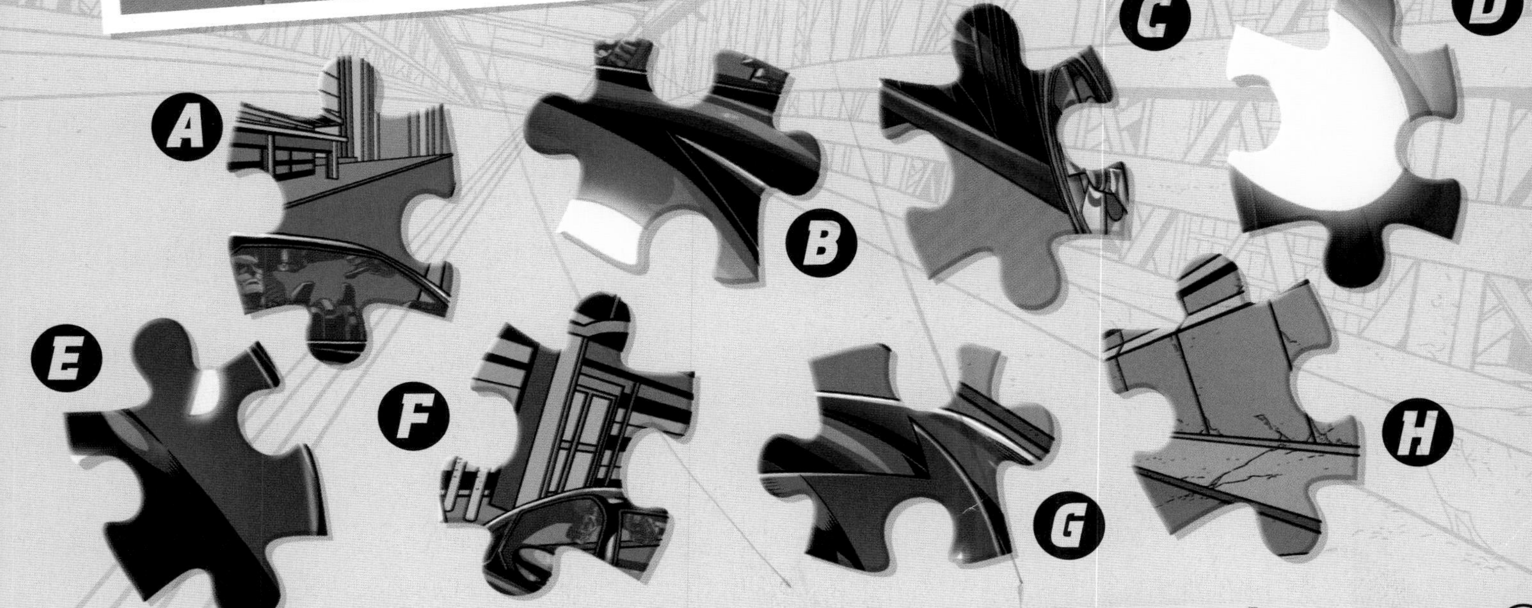

Answer on page 69

13

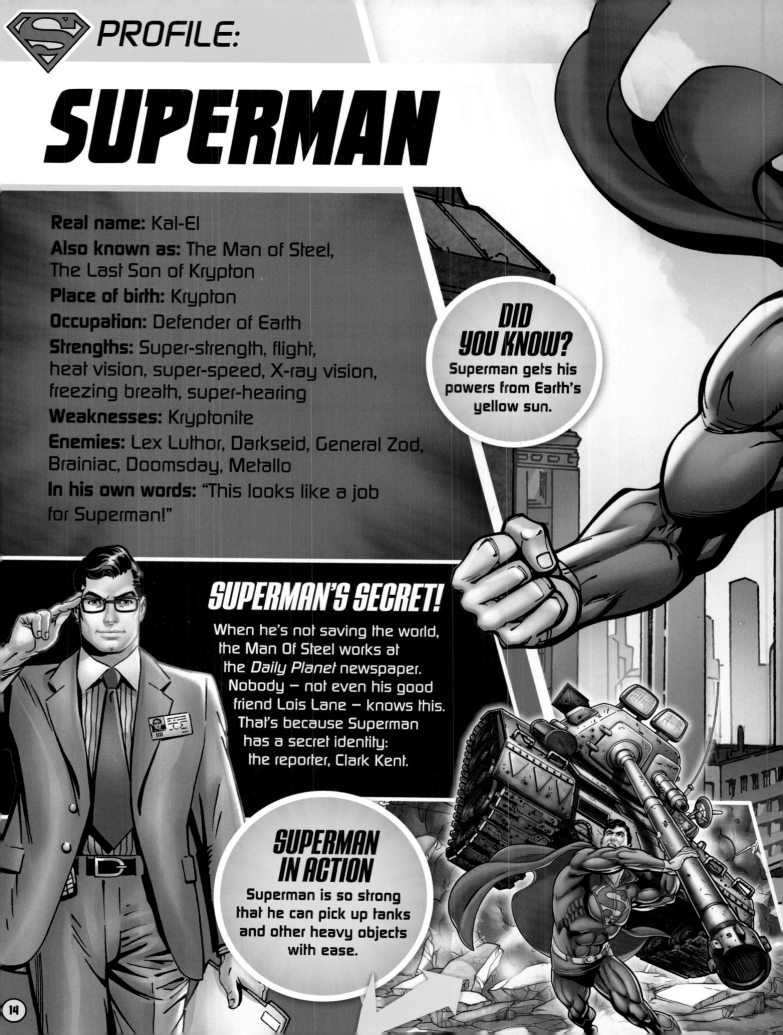

SUPERMAN

Real name: Kal-El

Also known as: The Man of Steel, The Last Son of Krypton

Place of birth: Krypton

Occupation: Defender of Earth

Strengths: Super-strength, flight, heat vision, super-speed, X-ray vision, freezing breath, super-hearing

Weaknesses: Kryptonite

Enemies: Lex Luthor, Darkseid, General Zod, Brainiac, Doomsday, Metallo

In his own words: "This looks like a job for Superman!"

DID YOU KNOW?

Superman gets his powers from Earth's yellow sun.

SUPERMAN'S SECRET!

When he's not saving the world, the Man Of Steel works at the *Daily Planet* newspaper. Nobody – not even his good friend Lois Lane – knows this. That's because Superman has a secret identity: the reporter, Clark Kent.

SUPERMAN IN ACTION

Superman is so strong that he can pick up tanks and other heavy objects with ease.

ODD HERO OUT

Which of these pictures of Superman is different from the others?

1

2

3

4

5

Answer on page 69

SUPERMAN SUDOKU

To defeat villains such as Lex Luthor and Doomsday, Superman and his friends need brains as well as brawn. Put your wits to the test by completing these puzzles.

HOW TO PLAY:

Fill in the blanks so that each row, column and square has one of each character. You can always write their names if drawing them is too tricky.

Answer on page 69

DID YOU KNOW?
The S in Superman's S-Shield doesn't stand for Superman. It's the crest of Kal-El's family and means 'hope'.

MAN OF STEEL WORD SEARCH

Is it a bird? Is it a plane? No, it's a Superman word search! Find the words at the bottom of the page in the grid below. Answers can run forwards, backwards, up, down and diagonally. Good luck!

```
T Y A D I J J J K F R E P U S D
O P D E A B U A W S A D T O I Y
B R A V E D S P F D A U T L R A
H D E R T E T Y P B S R A S H H
G A L O U E I X L A U A A Q A E
A D A K A I C W A T E I A D M R
A V B F R R E T H T L X R Y R O
F D Q W C Y E W S A A F B P L U
O F T B V Q P W D P O G L R P F
R V E O I U A T A K R D T O V C
T O P P J P C L O A T F A T R G
R P A P V Z X E W N K D F E Y N
E K C A I H D Z D G O C V C I O
S N C G P L A U S A F D Y T O R
S A E L L I V L L A M S A O P T
Y T A U Y O E A C H V J A R L S
```

HERO	BRAVE
KRYPTON	TRUTH
SUPER	FORTRESS
CAPE	JUSTICE
PROTECTOR	ALIAS
SMALLVILLE	STRONG

Answer on page 69

STARRO AND STRIPES FOREVER

Bruce Wayne's martial arts training is interrupted by startling news.

"This is a breaking story, direct from the Oval Office. The President of the United States demands a Declaration of Independence from super heroes today, the Fourth of July. The nation will no longer accept their assistance in fighting crime. Any future super hero activities have been outlawed."

Bruce is suspicious. As Batman, he boards the Batplane. He flicks several switches and is boosted with faster-than-light speed to Washington, DC.

In the White House briefing room, Clark Kent is reporting on the staggering story for the *Daily Planet* newspaper. His friend Diana Prince, a government employee, sits with him.

Clark scans the room with his powerful X-ray vision. He discovers a Starro probe on the president's neck! The leader of the free world is controlled by alien foe Starro the Conqueror!

Just then, Batman lands the Batplane on the National Mall.

Knowing something sinister is behind the president's shocking announcement, Clark and Diana race outside. Clark changes into his alter ego, Superman, as Diana whirls to transform herself into Wonder Woman.

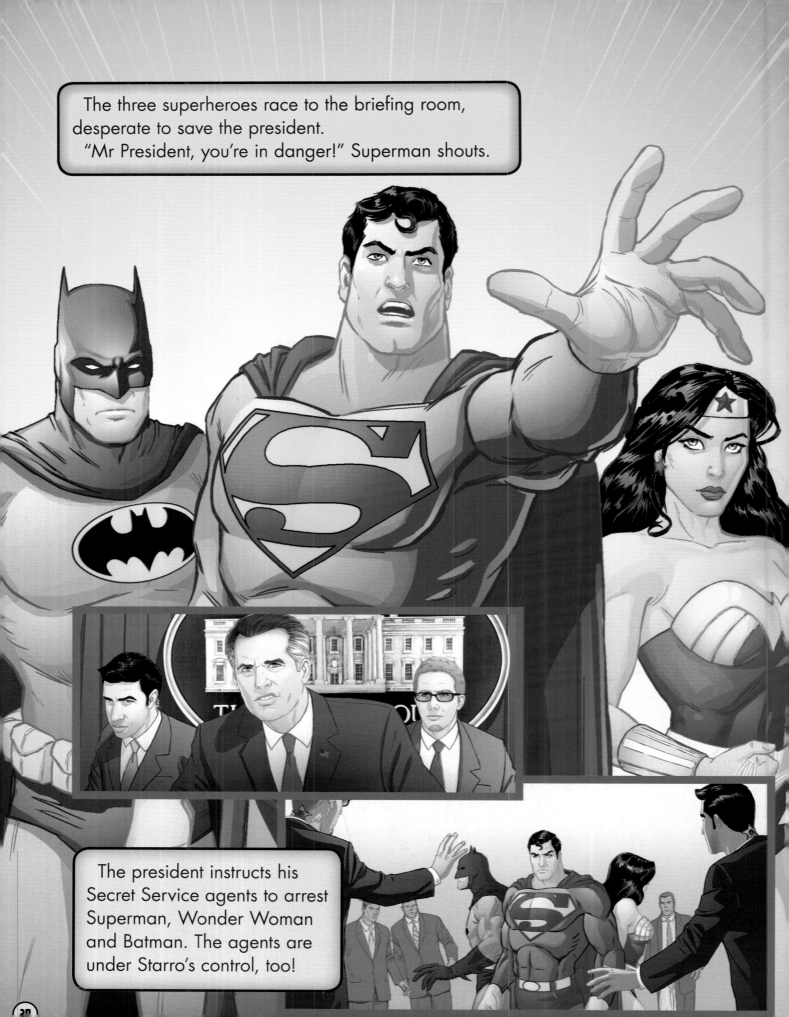

The three superheroes race to the briefing room, desperate to save the president.
"Mr President, you're in danger!" Superman shouts.

The president instructs his Secret Service agents to arrest Superman, Wonder Woman and Batman. The agents are under Starro's control, too!

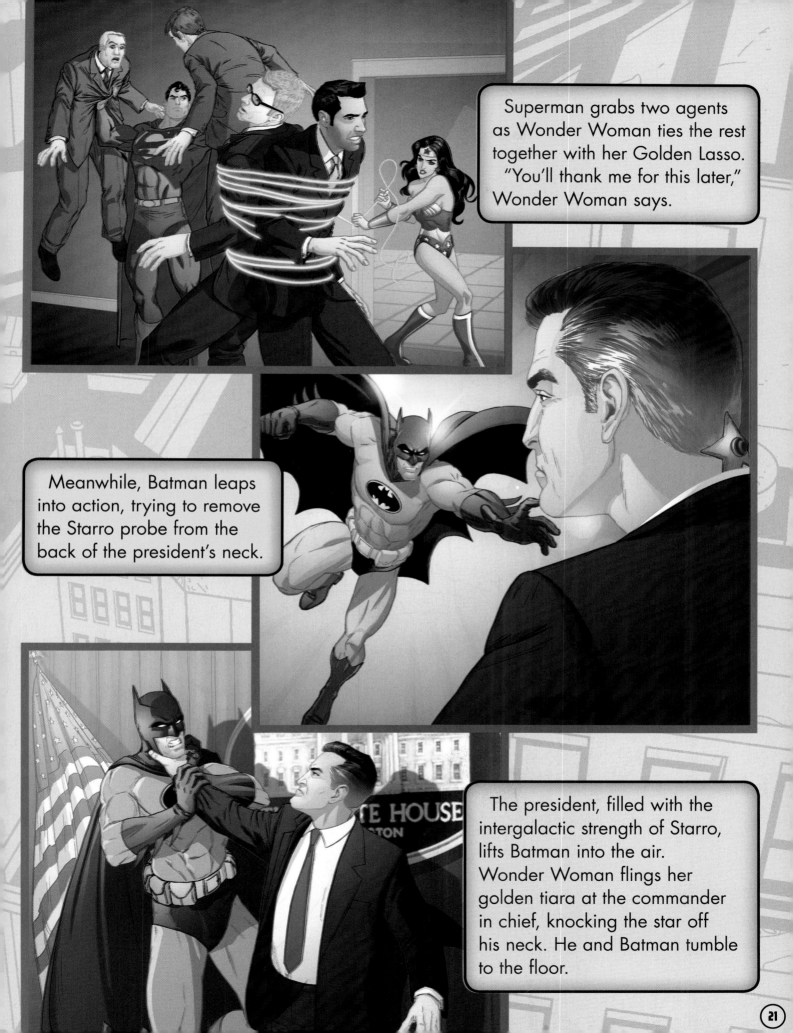

Superman grabs two agents as Wonder Woman ties the rest together with her Golden Lasso. "You'll thank me for this later," Wonder Woman says.

Meanwhile, Batman leaps into action, trying to remove the Starro probe from the back of the president's neck.

The president, filled with the intergalactic strength of Starro, lifts Batman into the air. Wonder Woman flings her golden tiara at the commander in chief, knocking the star off his neck. He and Batman tumble to the floor.

As the president regains his senses, Superman looks out of the window to see Starro the Conqueror moving across the sky. The Man of Steel races to catch the villain.

As Batman and Wonder Woman remove the probes from the confused Secret Service agents, military helicopters swoop around Superman on all sides, firing lasers at him.

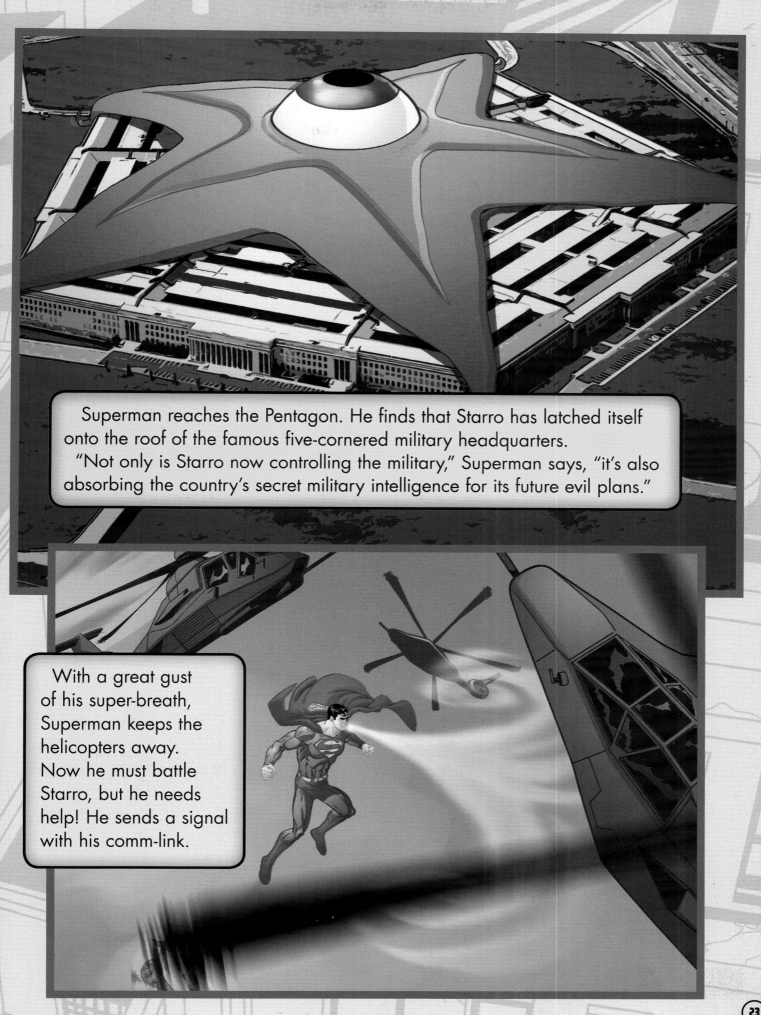

Superman reaches the Pentagon. He finds that Starro has latched itself onto the roof of the famous five-cornered military headquarters.

"Not only is Starro now controlling the military," Superman says, "it's also absorbing the country's secret military intelligence for its future evil plans."

With a great gust of his super-breath, Superman keeps the helicopters away. Now he must battle Starro, but he needs help! He sends a signal with his comm-link.

Batman takes to the sky in his Batplane. Wonder Woman flies next to him in her Invisible Jet. At the Pentagon, Superman has been using his heat vision on Starro to stop it from carrying out its evil plans.

Wonder Woman flings her Golden Lasso down, wrapping it around one of Starro's gigantic arms. Batman pilots his Batplane just above the great starfish and fires a missile at Starro, stunning it.

With Starro weaker now, Batman is able to use his shrink-ray to reduce Starro to the size of an ordinary starfish. Superman zooms into space with the villain.

With Starro defeated, the men and women of the military are finally free of its mind control.

Back at the White House, Superman, Wonder Woman and Batman enjoy the fireworks with the president and his family. "Thanks to the three of you, America today can still celebrate its freedom," the president says. "Happy Fourth of July!"

The End

PROFILE:

WONDER WOMAN

Real name: Diana Of Themyscira

Also known as: Princess Diana, Amazon Princess, Diana Prince

Place of birth: Themyscira (also known as Paradise Island)

Occupation: Government agent, ambassador, warrior princess of the Amazons

Strengths: Super-speed, flight, great wisdom

Weaknesses: Vulnerable to piercing weapons such as arrows and swords

Enemies: Cheetah, Circe, Ares

In her own words: "Great Hera!"

DID YOU KNOW?
Wonder Woman's most prized possession is her Golden Lasso. Anyone she captures with it is forced to tell the truth. She also has an Invisible Jet.

WONDER WOMAN IN ACTION
Wonder Woman's trademark bulletproof bracelets combined with her incredible speed mean she can fend off almost any attack.

WARRIOR PRINCESS

CREATE AND COLOUR SOME AMAZING NEW ARMOUR FOR **WONDER WOMAN.**

VISION QUEST

How many times does Wonder Woman's sword appear here? Tick the box with the correct number.

9   **16**   **14**

Answer on page 69

28

OUT OF SORTS

Wonder Woman is a little mixed up. Can you piece her back together? Write the correct order in the stars at the bottom. The first one has been done for you.

1, F

Answer on page 69

GREEN LANTERN

Real name: Harold 'Hal' Jordan

Also known as: The Emerald Warrior, The Galactic Guardian

Place of birth: Coast City

Occupation: Galactic Guardian

Strengths: Green Lantern's Power Ring enables him to do almost anything: from flying to creating objects out of pure energy

Weaknesses: The colour yellow

Enemies: Sinestro, Parallax

In his own words:
"In brightest day, in blackest night, no evil shall escape my sight!"

GREEN LANTERN IN ACTION

Green Lantern's Power Ring is fuelled by willpower. It can create giant green fists or emerald rifles capable of hitting their target from huge distances.

DID YOU KNOW?

Hal Jordan was originally a test pilot. He became a galactic police officer after meeting a dying alien.

MYSTERY MEMO

Green Lantern has been sent a mysterious coded message - but who is it from and what does it say? Help The Emerald Guardian find out by using the key below.

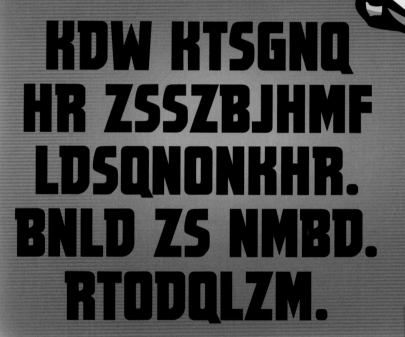

KDW KTSGNQ
HR ZSSZBJHMF
LDSQNONKHR.
BNLD ZS NMBD.
RTODQLZM.

WRITE THE MESSAGE HERE!

....
....
....
....
....
....

KEY

A	B	C	D	E	F	G	H	I	J	K	L	M
B	C	D	E	F	G	H	I	J	K	L	M	N

N	O	P	Q	R	S	T	U	V	W	X	Y	Z
O	P	Q	R	S	T	U	V	W	X	Y	Z	A

Answer on page 69

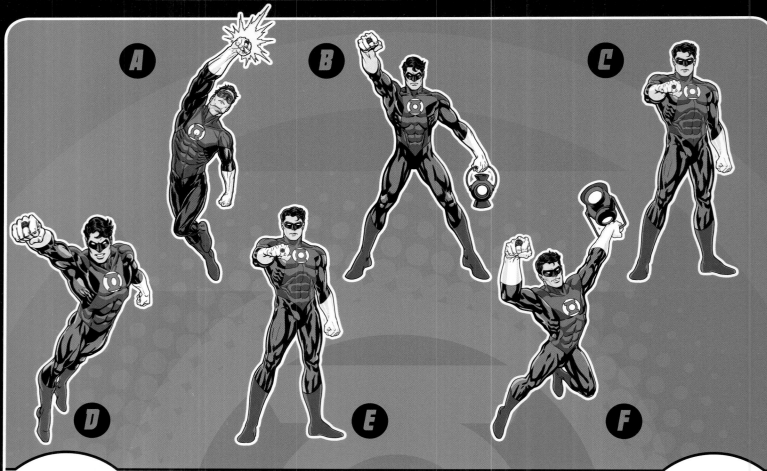

POWER PAIRS

Find the six pairs of matching Green Lanterns!

Answer on page 69

RING ROBBER

Green Lantern's Power Ring has been stolen by one of these four baddies. Use the clues below to work out the thief's identity.

The Joker

Lex Luthor

Catwoman

Scarecrow

THE THIEF IS A MAN.

THE THIEF HAS A PURPLE AND GREEN OUTFIT.

THE THIEF IS HOLDING SOMETHING.

THE THIEF IS:

....

Answer on page 69

THE RETURN OF STARRO

One day in Metropolis, Clark Kent went to interview the police chief. But when Clark arrived at the station, he knew something was wrong. All of the police officers were standing around their office, completely still. Nobody moved! One of the officers looked at Clark with a strange, blank stare.

"I know that look," said Clark.

He turned the officer round and, just as Clark had suspected, there was a small starfish stuck to the back of his neck.

Clark checked each officer – they all had a starfish!

"Starro!" he cried.

Clark knew he had to act fast.

"This looks like a job for Superman!"

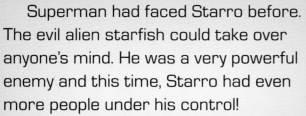

Superman had faced Starro before. The evil alien starfish could take over anyone's mind. He was a very powerful enemy and this time, Starro had even more people under his control!

Superman needed help, so he called his friends Batman and Wonder Woman. Starro had struck their cities, too!

"Starro has cloned himself and sent his legion to destroy our cities," said Batman. "To stop him, we'll need help!" Wonder Woman knew who to call.

Just a few minutes later, Superman, Batman and Wonder Woman were with some new friends – The Flash, Aquaman, Martian Manhunter and Green Lantern.

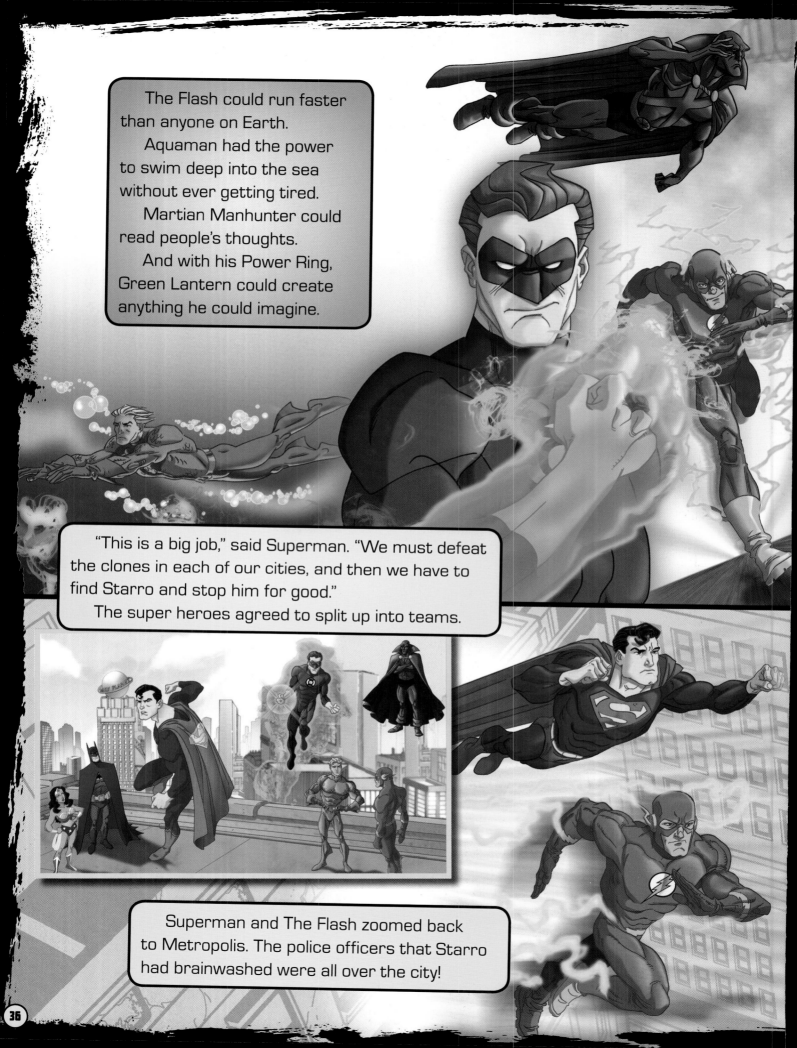

The Flash could run faster than anyone on Earth.

Aquaman had the power to swim deep into the sea without ever getting tired.

Martian Manhunter could read people's thoughts.

And with his Power Ring, Green Lantern could create anything he could imagine.

"This is a big job," said Superman. "We must defeat the clones in each of our cities, and then we have to find Starro and stop him for good."

The super heroes agreed to split up into teams.

Superman and The Flash zoomed back to Metropolis. The police officers that Starro had brainwashed were all over the city!

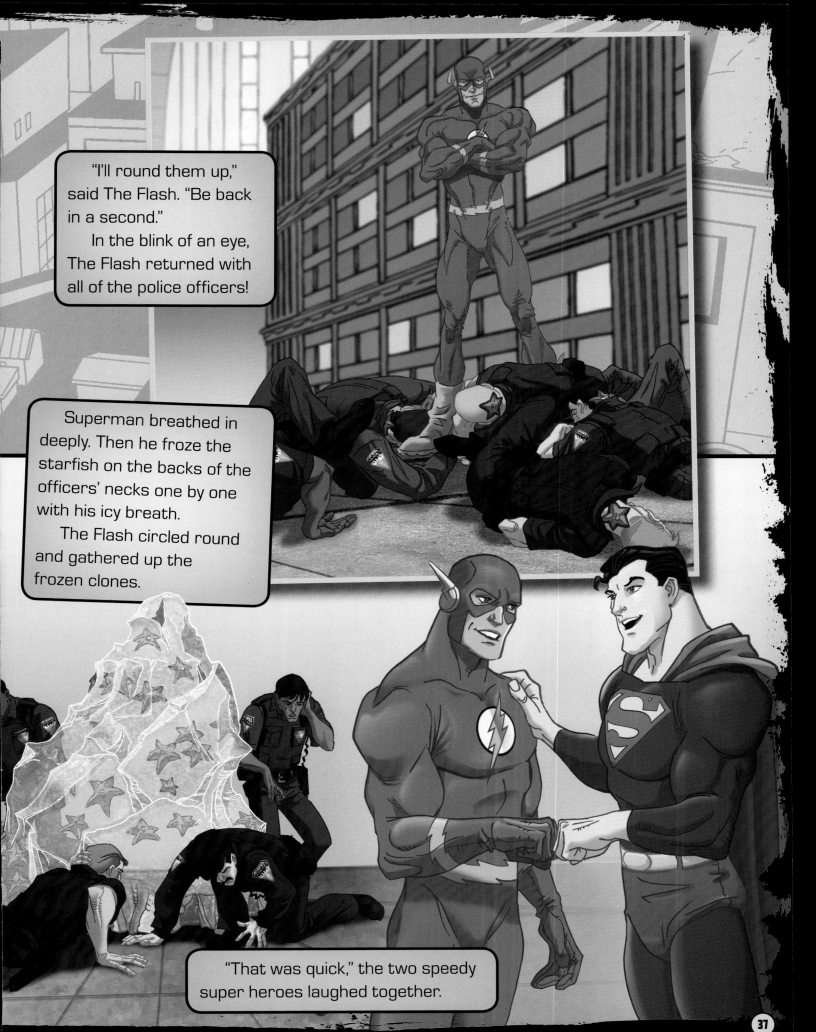

"I'll round them up," said The Flash. "Be back in a second."

In the blink of an eye, The Flash returned with all of the police officers!

Superman breathed in deeply. Then he froze the starfish on the backs of the officers' necks one by one with his icy breath.

The Flash circled round and gathered up the frozen clones.

"That was quick," the two speedy super heroes laughed together.

The Flash and Superman raced over to Gotham City. Batman had located all of the clones there with his Batcomputer.

Thanks to The Flash's speed, Superman's freeze breath and Batman's combat skills, they had the clones collected in no time.

Meanwhile, in Washington, D.C., Green Lantern used his Power Ring to find and gather the brainwashed police officers. Wonder Woman snared one in her Lasso of Truth.

"Tell me where Starro is," Wonder Woman said. "He's in the depths of the sea," said the officer.

"We'll see about that," said Wonder Woman.

"Martian Manhunter, do you copy?" she asked in her mind.

"Got it," said Martian Manhunter. He and Wonder Woman had linked their minds.

"Time to hit the beach," the alien hero told Aquaman.

Martian Manhunter sent the rest of the super heroes a mental message. They all met at the edge of the sea.

Aquaman dived into the water and swam as fast as a shark. There, in the murky depths of the sea, he found the evil starfish.

Aquaman grabbed Starro by an arm and pulled him up to the surface.

Green Lantern used his ring to help lift Starro out of the sea, and then Superman froze the villain with his icy breath.

"Time to get rid of this pest," said Martian [Ma]nhunter.

[H]e and Superman grabbed Starro and [his] clones and flew them to outer space. [Sup]erman used his super-breath to scatter [the] starfish all over the galaxy!

Back on Earth, the super heroes celebrated.
"Nothing like teamwork to keep the planet safe!" Batman said.

The End

PROFILE:
THE FLASH

Real name: Barry Allen

Also known as: The Fastest Man Alive, The Scarlet speedster

Place of birth: Central City

Occupation: Forensic scientist

Strengths: Super-speed and super-agility

Weaknesses: Vulnerable to telepathic attacks

Enemies: Gorilla Grodd, Trickster, Zoom

In his own words:
"I'm the fastest man alive."

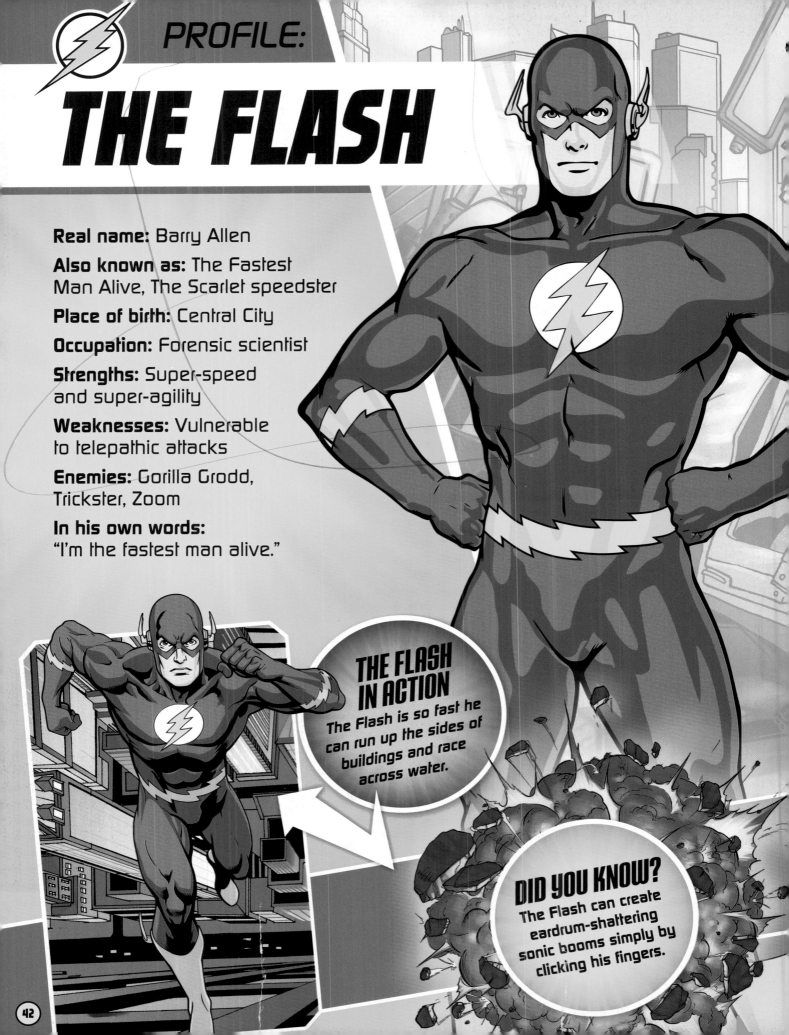

THE FLASH IN ACTION
The Flash is so fast he can run up the sides of buildings and race across water.

DID YOU KNOW?
The Flash can create eardrum-shattering sonic booms simply by clicking his fingers.

THE FLASH DASH

Place your finger on START, then plot a trail through the 'speedy' words. Avoid the 'slow' ones and you'll have finished ... in a flash!

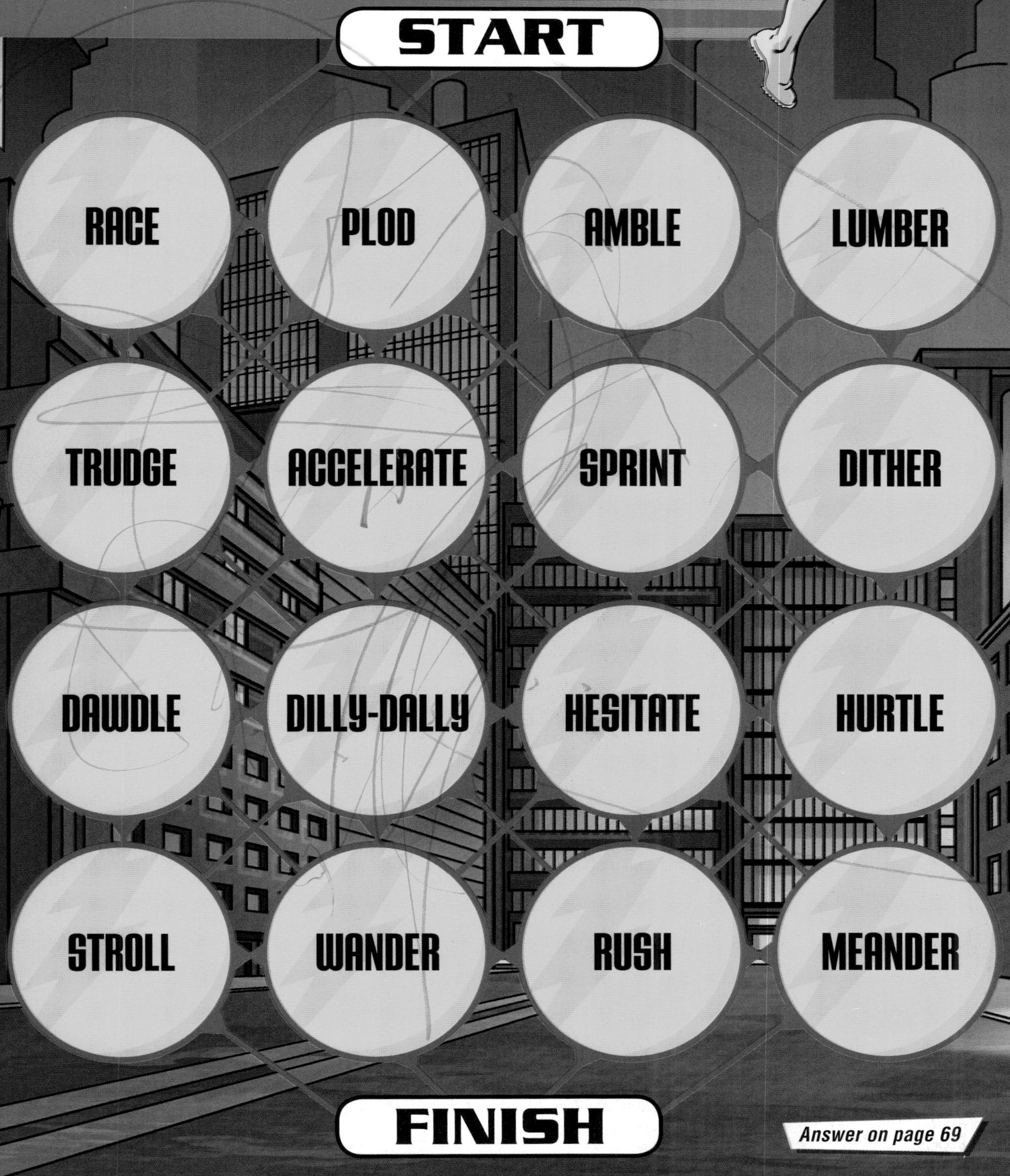

START

RACE

PLOD

AMBLE

LUMBER

TRUDGE

ACCELERATE

SPRINT

DITHER

DAWDLE

DILLY-DALLY

HESITATE

HURTLE

STROLL

WANDER

RUSH

MEANDER

FINISH

Answer on page 69

SPOT THE SPEEDSTER

How quickly can you find The Flash in this picture?

Answer on page 69

Answer on page 69

BONUS PUZZLE!
How many words can you make out of **THE FASTEST MAN ALIVE**? We've done one to get you started.

NAIL

....

....

44

NEED FOR SPEED

Aquaman and Cyborg need The Flash's help! Which path will lead the speedy super hero to his friends?

A   B   C

Answer on page 69

ALIEN INVADERS

Earth is under siege from aliens and it's up to the Justice League to save the day. Sketch the team fighting the interstellar attackers!

PREPARE FOR BATTLE

Wonder Woman is putting Superman, Green Lantern and The Flash through their paces. Look carefully at each sequence and then decide which picture comes next. Write the letters in the white boxes.

A   B   C

1   a

2

3

Answer on page 69

48

CROSSING THE ENEMY

So many criminals, so little time to catch them! Fit these Justice League foes into the word grid below. Ignore any spaces in their names - just include the letters.

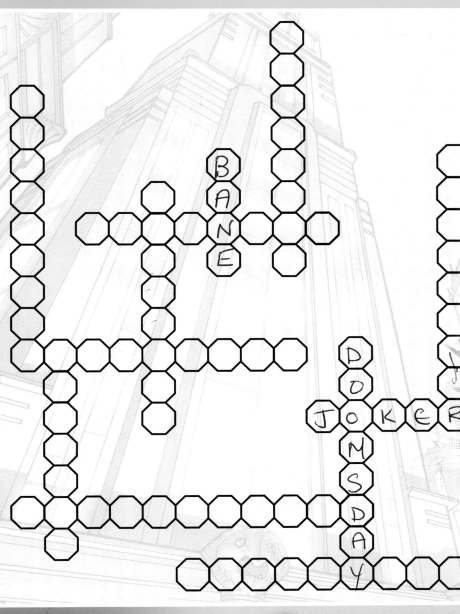

Grid entries filled in: BANE (vertical), DOOMSDAY (vertical), JOKER (horizontal)

DID YOU KNOW?
Scarecrow uses fear gas, which makes nightmares seem real!

 **JOKER** 5

 **LEX LUTHOR** 9

 **CATWOMAN** 8

 **BRAINIAC** 8

 ATROCITUS 9

 **CAPTAIN COLD** 11

SCARECROW 9

 **DOOMSDAY** 8

 DARKSEID 8

 BANE 4

 CHEETAH 7

 HARLEY QUINN 11

Answer on page 69

49

DAY OF THE UNDEAD

At midnight, a dark shadow enters the halls of Stonechat Museum. It is none other than the paranormal pilferer, Gentleman Ghost. He glides towards the display case of an ancient Aztec artifact, passing his phantom limb through the glass and removing the relic.

"This little item is the missing ingredient in my recipe for world devastation!" he cackles. Then the wicked wraith phases through the wall and disappears into the moonless night.

The next morning, Carter and Shiera Hall, archaeologists, discover the puzzling theft. They contact their friend Batman. "This residue is paranormal," the super hero says. "Our thief has supernatural abilities beyond science and reason."

"Carter and I will help you catch the culprit," Shiera says. "As Hawkman and Hawkgirl!"

Meanwhile, in Gotham City, the parade for the **Dia de los Muertos**, or Day of the Dead, is about to commence. Jaime Reyes is in town to enjoy the festivities. "I am **so** looking forward to a few days off from being Blue Beetle," he says to himself. "Fighting crime can leave you feeling dead tired!"

Little does the young hero know that his holiday is about to get cut short....

At the head of the parade, a ghoul appears — much to the delight of the crowd. But their cheers turn to screams when the beast punches through a float!

"Whoa! That's not in the programme," Jaime says. The scarab attached to his spine informs the hero that the ghoul is Solomon Grundy, a super-strong zombie who resides in a swamp outside the city.

As the mindless menace creates chaos, Jamie quickly ducks into an empty alley....

"Guess I'm working after all," he says and transforms into the **BLUE BEETLE!**

Blue Beetle flies towards Solomon Grundy and zaps the beast. This further enrages the zombie and he charges towards the hero. Blue Beetle lures Grundy away from the people. "I will squish you, little bug!" snarls Solomon Grundy. "Little? I'm not little!" yells Blue Beetle before he is cornered. "Uh-oh," he gulps.

Suddenly, three blurs zip by overhead. Members of the Justice League have arrived! Batman, Hawkman and Hawkgirl swoop down to aid their teammate.

"You're going to give up, Grundy," Batman says. "With or without a fight."

"Look at it this way," Hawkman adds. "You're outnumbered AND outmuscled."

"It's your choice," says Hawkgirl.

Grundy roars with rage. He smashes the support beam of the elevated platform holding the ceremony's officials. They topple from the structure. Batman shoots his grappling hook around the beams, slowing the descent of the tower. Blue Beetle, Hawkman and Hawkgirl soar into the air, swiftly rescuing the falling people.

During the confusion, Solomon Grundy slips away unnoticed.

"How did you know there was trouble?" Blue Beetle asks Batman.

"My readings showed a high level of paranormal activity at this location," Batman states.

"Is Grundy responsible for stealing the artifact?" Hawkman asks.

"No, he's not smart enough," Batman replies. "But by following his trail, we'll find the real mastermind!"

Meanwhile, in a large cemetery on the outskirts of Gotham City, Gentleman Ghost hovers near a grave. He holds up the artifact and recites an ancient incantation. The relic glows, releasing beams of eerie light. "Yes!" the ghoul cries. "The REAL Day of the Dead is about to dawn!"

Solomon Grundy finds Gentleman Ghost in the midst of his magic spell. Suddenly, decrepit corpse fingers claw their way out of the dirt. The dead are rising from their graves! "Thank you, my swamp-dwelling subordinate," Gentleman Ghost says to Grundy. "Your distraction at the parade bought me enough time to work my malicious magic."

Meanwhile, the Justice League follows the increasing levels of paranormal energy straight to the cemetery. They are met with a shocking sight: legions of groaning zombies shuffle towards them with their rotted arms outstretched.

"Remarkable!" Hawkman exclaims. "Whoever is behind this used the artifact to reanimate the deceased."

"Yeah, and that someone is taking the Day of the Dead WAY too seriously," Blue Beetle says nervously.

"It is I, Gentleman Ghost, who orchestrated this evil event!" the villain shouts. Then he turns to his army. "My minions! Destroy the Justice League so they may join our undead ranks!"

"The artifact controls the zombies," Batman says. "We must retrieve it!"

"We'll keep these baddies busy. You go for the ghost!" says Hawkman.

He and Hawkgirl fly up into the sky. They dive down into the fray, blasting back Grundy and the zombie horde. Batman and Blue Beetle leap through the clearing and chase after Gentleman Ghost.

The Caped Crusader hurls a Batarang with expert accuracy, knocking the artifact from the ghost's clutches. "NOOO!" the ghoul yells. With the psychic connection severed, the horrifying spell is broken.

Directionless, the zombies sink back into the ground. Now released from mind control, Solomon Grundy retreats to his swamp.

"You and I have unfinished business," Blue Beetle yells after the big brute....

"Let him go, Blue Beetle, and let's stop the real culprit," Batman says, pointing to the fleeing phantom.

"You're right," says Blue Beetle, shooting a burst of energy around the villain. "This impenetrable alien force field has a special setting for all manner of apparitions and spectres. You're toast, ghost!"

Aztec artifact to Hawkgirl.
"The artifact will return to the museum, but what will happen to Gentleman Ghost?" Hawkgirl asks.

"He's going to spend his afterlife in a very uncomfortable containment unit at S.T.A.R. Labs in Metropolis," Blue Beetle answers and speeds off.

With disaster averted, Blue Beetle returns to his friends and says, "Hey, let's go to the parade. I'm back on holiday, and we're already dressed for the occasion!" The heroes laugh and join their friend. Together with the citizens of Gotham City, the Justice League enjoys the festivities. The Day of the Dead celebration has become a night to remember!

The End

FREEZE FRAME!

Look at this fight scene between The Flash, Green Lantern and Captain Cold for 60 seconds. Then cover up the picture and try to answer the five questions correctly.

1. What is Captain Cold holding in his hand?
2. True or false – the fight is taking place in a city.
3. The Flash is A) leaping B) running C) sliding.
4. What colour are Captain Cold's slitted shades?
5. True or false – Green Lantern isn't wearing his Power Ring.

Answer on page 69

WANTED: GALAXY DEFENDER

The Justice League is recruiting!
Draw a new super hero to join the team.
Remember to give him or her a cool name.

My super hero is called:

DOUBLE TROUBLE!

There are six differences between these two pictures of Green Lantern, Superman and Brainiac. How quickly can you find them?

Answer on page 69

DID YOU KNOW?

Superman has a secret home in the Arctic. It's called the Fortress Of Solitude.

COMIC CREATOR!

Create your very own comic strip by writing in the speech bubbles on the pictures below!

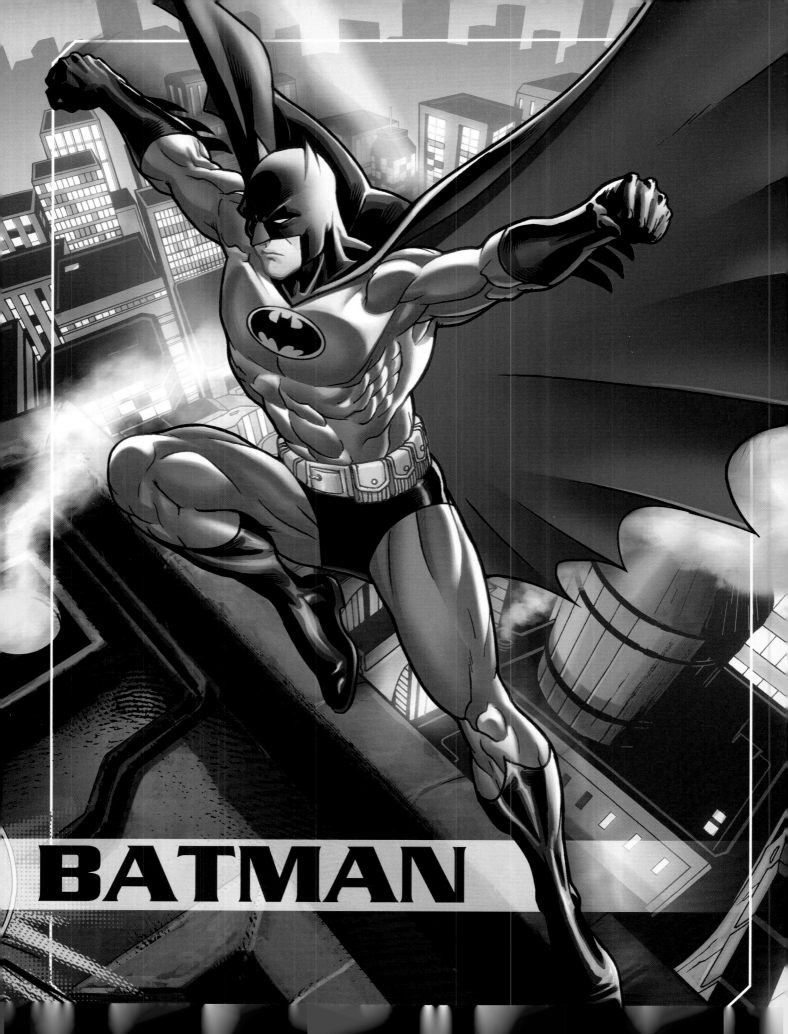

GREEN LANTERN

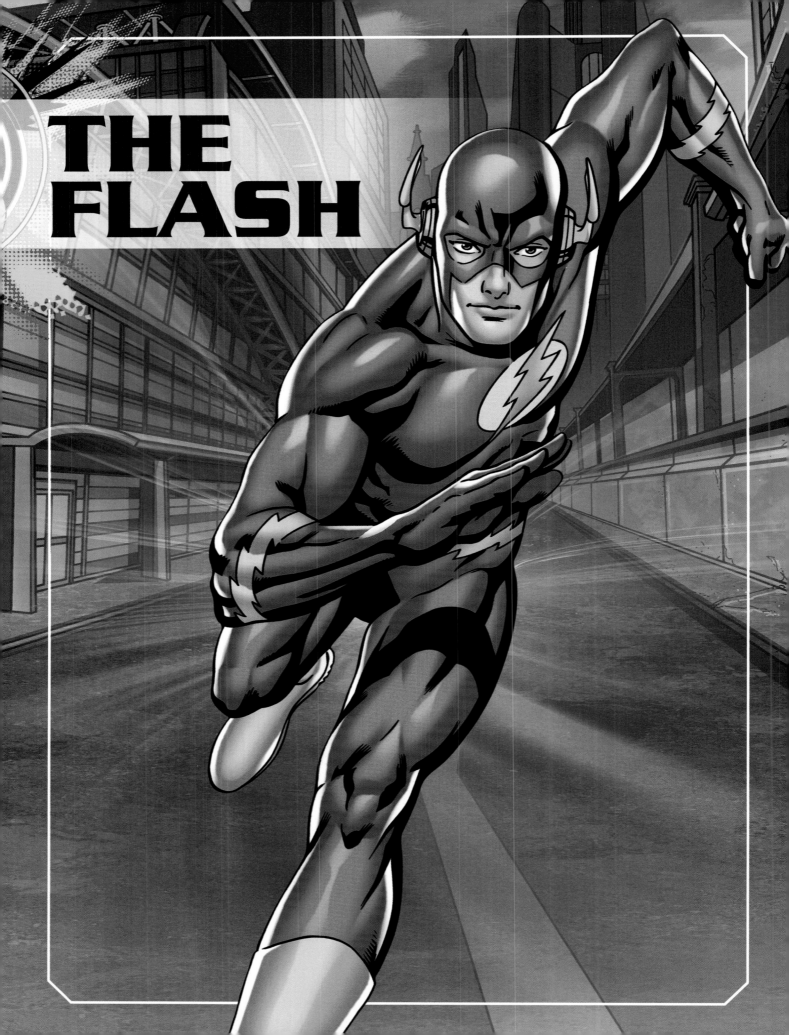

THE FLASH

ANSWERS

Pages 8-9
BATTER UP! 10

Page 11
KNIGHT WATCH B

Page 12
SIGN OF THE CRIMES

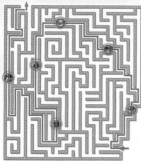

Page 13
MISSING IN ACTION! 1-C, 2-B, 3-E

Page 15
ODD HERO OUT 4

Page 16
SUPERMAN SUDOKU

Page 17
MAN OF STEEL WORD SEARCH

```
T Y A D I J J J K F R E P U S D
O P D E A B U A W S A D T O I Y
B R A V E D S P F D A U T L R A
H D E R T E T Y P B S R A S H H
G A L O U E I X L A U A A Q A E
A D A K A I C W A T E I A D S R
A V B F R R E T H T L X R Y R O
F D Q D C Y E W S A A F B P L U
O F T B V O P W D P O G L R P F
R U E O I U A T A K R D T O V C
T O P P J P C L O A T F A T R G
R P A P V Z X E W N K D F E Y N
E K C A I H D Z D G O C V C I O
S N C G P L A U S A F D Y T O R
S A E L L I V L L A M S A O P T
Y T A U Y O E A C H V J A R L S
```

Page 28
VISION QUEST 14

Page 29
OUT OF SORTS

1-F, 2-D, 3-B, 4-E, 5-A, 6-C

Page 31
MYSTERY MEMO

LEX LUTHOR IS ATTACKING METROPOLIS. COME AT ONCE. SUPERMAN.

Page 32
POWER PAIRS

A&J, B&K, C&E, D&H, F&I, G&L

Page 33
RING ROBBER *The Joker*

Page 43
THE FLASH DASH

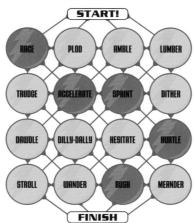

Page 44
SPOT THE SPEEDSTER

Page 45
NEED FOR SPEED A

Page 48
PREPARE FOR BATTLE

1-C, 2-B, 3-A

Page 49
CROSSING THE ENEMY

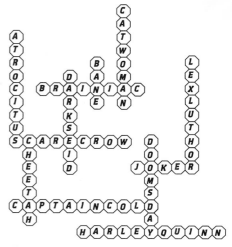

Page 59
FREEZE FRAME!

1. His cold gun
2. False
3. B) Running
4. White
5. False

Page 62
DOUBLE TROUBLE!